Published by Ladybird Books Ltd
80 Strand London WC2R 0RL
A Penguin Company
9 10

Printed in Italy

DISNEP

POCAHONTAS

Ladybird

The English sailing ship, the *Susan Constant,* was heading towards the New World – America.

The leader of the expedition, Governor John Ratcliffe, stood on deck holding his pampered pug dog, Percy. "There's gold in the New World," Ratcliffe said to himself. "And soon it will all be *mine!*"

Nearby, stood the brave Captain John Smith. He had been on many exciting voyages before and was looking forward to the start of a new adventure.

Meanwhile, high on a cliff in the New World, stood a young Indian girl called Pocahontas, meaning 'Little Mischief'. As always, Meeko, an inquisitive raccoon, and Flit, a tiny hummingbird, were nearby.

"Hurry! Your father is waiting," called Pocahontas' friend, Nakoma, from her canoe in the river below. Pocahontas dived into the deep blue water and the two friends paddled homewards.

Back at the Indian village, Pocahontas' father, Chief Powhatan, had some wonderful news for his daughter. "The brave warrior, Kocoum, has asked for your hand in marriage," he said. "I will give you the necklace your mother wore at our wedding so that you may wear it at yours."

Pocahontas wanted to obey her father's wishes but Kocoum was so… *serious*! She decided to go to the enchanted glade where she could talk to the ancient tree spirit, Grandmother Willow.

Pocahontas told Grandmother Willow about Kocoum. She also told the wise spirit about a strange dream she kept having about a spinning arrow.

"The arrow is pointing you down your path," said Grandmother Willow. "Listen to the spirits of the earth, the water and the sky and they will guide you."

Just then, Pocahontas felt the wind blowing through her hair. She climbed high into Grandmother Willow's branches to hear what it was telling her. As she looked out to sea, Pocahontas saw what seemed to be strange clouds in the distance – they were the sails of a ship.

Pocahontas leapt down and ran over to a rocky ledge to get a closer look. She saw that the ship had dropped anchor and that men were coming ashore. One was tall and handsome – and he was heading straight towards her! It was John Smith.

As Pocahontas watched, the stranger climbed onto the rocky ledge and looked out across the beautiful landscape. Before Pocahontas could stop Meeko he had scampered over to meet the stranger. "Hello, little fellow," Smith said, kindly, handing a biscuit to the raccoon.

Just then, someone called Smith's name and he climbed down from the ledge. Pocahontas was left wondering about the mysterious stranger. She decided to follow him to find out more…

Later that day, as Smith explored the New World, he came to a sparkling waterfall. On the other side of the cascading water he saw a young Indian girl – Pocahontas.

For a long moment neither he nor Pocahontas moved. They stared at each other and knew they were falling in love.

That afternoon, Pocahontas taught Smith a few words of her language. Smith had thought that the Indians would be savages but meeting Pocahontas changed his mind. He learnt that her people loved the land and lived in harmony with it.

While they talked, Meeko nuzzled through Smith's bag looking for another biscuit. Instead, he found Smith's compass, which he carried off to a nearby tree. He would find a hiding place for this little treasure!

Meanwhile, Governor Ratcliffe had ordered his men to begin digging for gold. "It's got to be here *somewhere*!" he roared as the settlers ripped up trees and dug up the ground.

Kocoum and another warrior, Namontack, were hiding in some nearby bushes. They watched in horror as their land was torn apart.

When the settlers discovered them there a fierce fight broke out and Namontack was badly wounded. Terrified, Kocoum carried his friend back to their village.

Later, when Pocahontas returned to the village, she found her people preparing for battle with the settlers. Their land was being destroyed by these invaders and now Namontack had been wounded. They had to be stopped.

"Please," Pocahontas begged her father, "try talking to the settlers instead of fighting them."

"They do not want to talk!" Chief Powhatan replied, sternly.

At that same moment, Smith was trying to convince Ratcliffe not to fight the Indians. But Ratcliffe was only interested in finding gold.

"This is *my* land now!" he cried. "And the Indians *must* be killed in order to get to the gold!"

That night, Pocahontas and Smith met in the enchanted glade, where she begged him to talk to her father. It was the only way to prevent a terrible battle. When Smith agreed Pocahontas was delighted and the two of them kissed.

But they didn't realise that they were not alone. Kocoum had followed Pocahontas, and Thomas, a young settler, had followed Smith.

Suddenly, Kocoum sprang from the bushes. Thomas, realising the warrior was about to attack Smith, fired his gun. As Kocoum fell he pulled Pocahontas' necklace from her neck. In an instant, he lay dead.

Indian war cries sounded in the distance. "You must go, Thomas!" Smith cried. The frightened young settler fled back to his camp.

Moments later, Indian warriors arrived
and captured Smith. They took him and
Kocoum's body back to their village. Chief
Powhatan, believing Smith was responsible
for Kocoum's death, ordered that Smith
be killed at sunrise.

Later, Pocahontas managed to sneak into the hut where Smith was being held prisoner.

"I'm so sorry," she wept. "If we had never met none of this would have happened. But I can't leave you now."

"You never will," Smith assured her. "No matter what happens to me I'll always be with you in my heart forever."

Heartbroken, Pocahontas went to see Grandmother Willow.

Suddenly, Meeko handed Pocahontas Smith's compass, which he had recovered from its hiding place.

As Pocahontas gazed at the needle of the compass she felt her heart leap. Now she understood – this was the spinning arrow from her dream! Pocahontas knew what she must do…

At the Indian village, Chief Powhatan held his club above Smith's head. The settlers, led by Ratcliffe, were approaching.

"Stop!" cried Pocahontas, racing forward and throwing herself across Smith's body to protect him. "If you kill him, you will have to kill me too! Look where hatred has brought us," she said.

Chief Powhatan suddenly realised his daughter was speaking the truth and ordered Smith's release.

As the Indians lowered their weapons Ratcliffe saw his chance. "Fire!" he cried. But the settlers were tired of his greed and cruelty. They also lowered their weapons.

Enraged, Ratcliffe grabbed a gun, aimed it at Chief Powhatan and fired. Smith bravely flung himself in front of the Chief and the bullet hit him instead.

The angry settlers surrounded Ratcliffe. They bound him in chains and marched him back to the *Susan Constant*.

A few days later, the *Susan Constant* was ready to set sail. The wounded Smith lay on a stretcher while Pocahontas knelt beside her. She was wearing her mother's necklace that Percy and Meeko had found in the wood.

Smith had to return to England if he was to survive. "I can't leave you here," he said.

"You never will," Pocahontas replied, reminding him of his own words. "I will always be with you in my heart *forever*."

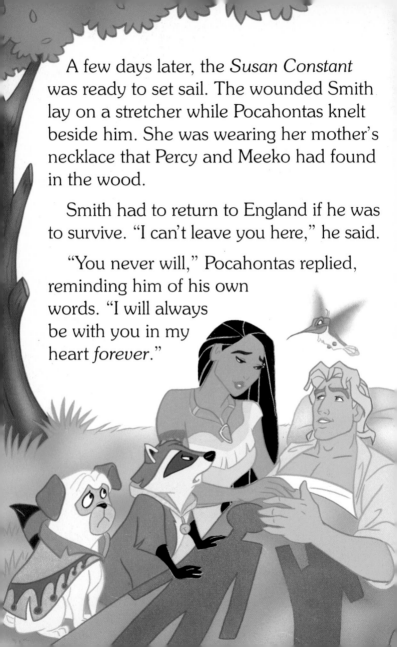

Pocahontas and John Smith had shown
that different peoples could live together
in peace but she knew that she must stay
to try and keep this new found friendship
and understanding alive. At last,
Pocahontas had found her one true path.